The Specialist

By

Charles (Chic) Sale

Publishers:
Specialist Publishing Company
Carmel
California

Twenty-second Printing

Foreword

Lem Putt—that wasn't his real name—really lived. He was just as sincere in his work as a great painter whose heart is in his canvas; and in this little sketch I have simply tried to bring to you recollections of a man I once knew, who was so rich in odd and likable traits of character as to make a most lasting impression on my memory.

CHARLES (CHIC) SALE.

The Specialist

Mr. President and Gentlemen:

*Y*ou've heerd a lot of pratin' and prattlin' about this bein' the age of specialization. I'm a carpenter by trade. At one time I could of built a house, barn, church or chicken coop. But I seen the need of a specialist in my line, so I studied her. I got her; she's mine. Gentlemen, you are face to face with the champion privy builder of Sangamon County.

Luke Harkins was my first customer. He heerd about me specializin' and decided to take a chance. I built fer him just the average eight family, three holer. With that job my reputation was made, and since then I have devoted all my time and thought to that special line. Of course, when business is slack, I do do a little paperhangin' on the side. But my heart is just in privy buildin'. And when I finish a job, I ain't through. I give all my customers six months' privy service free gratis. I explained this to Luke, and one day he calls me up and sez: "Lem, I wish you'd come out here; I'm havin' privy trouble."

So I gits in the car and drives out to Luke's place, and hid behind them Baldwins, where I could get a good view of the situation.

It was right in the middle of hayin' time, and them hired hands was goin' in there and stayin' anywheres from forty minutes to an hour. Think of that!

I sez: "Luke, you sure have got privy trouble." So I takes out my kit of tools and goes in to examine the structure.

First I looks at the catalogue hangin' there, thinkin' it might be that; but it wasn't even from a reckonized house.

Then I looks at the seats proper, and I
see what the trouble was. I had made
them holes too durn comfortable. So I
gets out a scroll saw and cuts 'em square
with hard edges. Then I go back and
takes up my position as before—me here,
the Baldwins here, and the privy there.
And I watched them hired hands goin' in
and out for nearly two hours! and not
one of them was stayin' more than four
minutes.

"Luke," I sez, "I've solved her." That's
what comes of bein' a specialist, gentlemen.

'Twarn't long after I built that twin
job for the school house, and then after
that the biggest plant up to date—a eight
holer. Elmer Ridgway was down and
looked it over. And he come to me one
day and sez: "Lem, I seen that eight hole
job you done down there at the Corners,
and it sure is a dandy; and figgerin' as
how I'm goin' to build on the old Robin-

son property, I thought I'd ask you to
kind of estimate on a job for me."

"You come to the right man, Elmer,"
I sez. "I'll be out as soon as I get the roof
on the two-seater I'm puttin' up for the
Sheriff."

Couple of days later I drives out to
Elmer's place, gettin' there about dinner
time. I knocks a couple of times on the
door and I see they got a lot of folks to
dinner, so not wishin' to disturb 'em, I
just sneaks around to the side door and
yells, "Hey, Elmer, here I am; where do
you want that privy put?"

Elmer comes out and we get to talkin'
about a good location. He was all fer
puttin' her right alongside a jagged path
runnin' by a big Northern Spy.

"I wouldn't do it, Elmer," I sez; "and
I'll tell you why. In the first place, her
bein' near a tree is bad. There ain't no
sound in nature so disconcertin' as the
sound of apples droppin' on th' roof.

"Some of them stayed nearly an
hour"

Then another thing, there's a crooked path runnin' by that tree and the soil there ain't adapted to absorbin' moisture. Durin' the rainy season she's likely to be slippery. Take your grandpappy—goin' out there is about the only recreation he gets. He'll go out some rainy night with his nighties flappin' around his legs, and like as not when you come out in the mornin' you'll find him prone in the mud, or maybe skidded off one of them curves and wound up in the corn crib. No sir," I sez, "put her in a straight line with the house and if it's all the same to you have her go past the woodpile. I'll tell you why.

"Take a woman, fer instance—out she goes. On the way back she'll gather five sticks of wood, and the average woman will make four or five trips a day. There's twenty sticks in the wood box without any trouble. On the other hand, take a timid woman, if she sees any men folks around, she's too bashful to go direct out so she'll go to the wood-pile, pick up the wood, go back to the house and watch her chance. The average timid woman—especially a new hired girl—I've knowed to make as many as ten trips to the wood-pile before she goes in, regardless. On a good day you'll have your wood box filled by noon, and right there is a savin' of time.

"Now, about the diggin' of her. You can't be too careful about that," I sez; "dig her deep and dig her wide. It's a mighty sight better to have a little privy over a big hole than a big privy over a little hole. Another thing; when you dig her deep you've got her dug; and you ain't got that disconcertin' thought stealin' over you that sooner or later you'll have to dig again.

"And when it comes to construction," I sez, "I can give you joists or beams. Joists make a good job. Beams cost a bit more, but they're worth it. Beams, you might say, will last forever. 'Course, I could give you joists, but take your Aunt Emmy, she ain't gettin' a mite lighter. Some day she might be out there when them joists give way and there she'd be—catched. Another thing you've got to figger on, Elmer," I sez, "is that Odd Fellows picnic in the fall. Them boys is goin' to get in there in fours and sixes, singin' and drinkin', and the like, and I want to tell you there's nothin' breaks up an Odd Fellows picnic quicker than a diggin' party. Beams, I say, every time, and rest secure.

"And about her roof," I sez. "I can give you a lean-to type or a pitch roof. Pitch roofs cost a little more, but some of our best people has lean-tos. If it was fer myself, I'd have a lean-to, and I'll tell you why.

"A lean-to has two less corners fer the wasps to build their nests in; and on a

hot August afternoon there ain't nothin'
so disconcertin' as a lot of wasps buzzin'
'round while you're settin' there doin' a
little readin', figgerin', or thinkin'. Another thing," I sez, "a lean-to gives you a
high door. Take that son of yours, shoot-
in' up like a weed; don't any of him seem
to be turnin' under. If he was tryin' to
get under a pitch roof door he'd crack his
head everytime. Take a lean-to, Elmer;
they ain't stylish, but they're practical.

"Now, about her furnishin's. I can give
you a nail or hook for the catalogue, and
besides, a box for cobs. You take your
pa, for instance; he's of the old school
and naturally he'd prefer the box; so put
'em both in, Elmer. Won't cost you a bit
more for the box and keeps peace in the
family. You can't teach an old dog new
tricks," I sez.

"And as long as we're on furnishin's,
I'll tell you about a technical point that
was put to me the other day. The question was this: 'What is the life, or how

long will the average mail order catalogue last, in just the plain, ordinary
eight family three holer?' It stumped me
for a spell; but this bein' a reasonable
question I checked up, and found that
by placin the catalogue in there, say in
January—when you get your new one—
you should be into the harness section by
June; but, of course, that ain't through
apple time, and not countin' on too many
city visitors, either.

"An' another thing — they've been
puttin' so many of those stiff colored
sheets in the catalogue here lately that
it makes it hard to figger. Somethin'
really ought to be done about this, and
I've thought about takin' it up with Mr.
Sears Roebuck hisself.

"As to the latch fer her. I can give you
a spool and a string, or a hook and eye.
The cost of a spool and string is practically nothin, but they ain't positive in
action. If somebody comes out and starts

"If it was me, Elmer, I'd say no windows;
and I'll tell you why."

rattlin the door, either the spool or the string is apt to give way, and there you are. But, with a hook and eye she's yours, you might say, for the whole afternoon, if you're so minded. Put on the hook and eye of the best quality 'cause there ain't nothin' that'll rack a man's nerves more than to be sittin' there ponderin', without a good, strong, substantial latch on the door." And he agreed with me.

"Now," I sez, "what about windows; some want 'em, some don't. They ain't so popular as they used to be. If it was me, Elmer, I'd say no windows; and I'll tell you why. Take, fer instance, somebody comin' out—maybe they're just in a hurry or maybe they waited too long. If the door don't open right away and you won't answer 'em, nine times out of ten they'll go 'round and 'round and look in the window, and you don't get the privacy you ought to.

"Now, about ventilators, or the designs

I cut in the doors. I can give you stars, diamonds, or crescents—there ain't much choice—all give good service. A lot of people like stars, because they throw a ragged shadder. Others like crescents cause they're graceful and simple. Last year we was cuttin' a lot of stars; but this year people are kinda quietin' down and runnin' more to crescents. I do cut twinin' hearts now and then for young married couples; and bunches of grapes for the newly rich. These last two designs come under the head of novelties and I don't very often suggest 'em, because it takes time and runs into money.

"I wouldn't take any snap judgment on her ventilators, Elmer," I sez, "because they've got a lot to do with the beauty of the structure. And don't over-do it, like Doc Turner did. He wanted stars and crescents both, against my better judgment, and now he's sorry. But it's too late; 'cause when I cut 'em, they're cut." And, gentlemen, you can get mighty tired, sittin' day after day lookin' at a ventilator that ain't to your likin'.

"Now," I sez, "how do you want that door to swing? Openin' in or out? He said he didn't know. So I sez it should open in. This is the way it works out: Place yourself in there. The door openin' in, say about forty-five degree. This gives you air and lets the sun beat in. Now, if you hear anybody comin', you can give it a quick shove with your foot and there you are. But if she swings out, where are you? You can't run the risk of havin' her open for air or sun, because if anyone comes, you can't get up off that seat, reach way around and grab 'er without gettin' caught, now can you?" He could see I was right.

So I built his door like all my doors, swingin' in, and, of course, facing east, to get the full benefit of th' sun. And I tell you, gentlemen, there ain't nothin' more restful than to get out there in the mornin', comfortably seated, with th' door about three-fourths open. The old sun, beatin' in on you, sort of relaxes a body — makes you feel m-i-g-h-t-y, m-i-g-h-t-y r-e-s-t-f-u-l.

"Now," I sez, "about the paintin' of her. What color do you want 'er, Elmer?" He said red. "Elmer," I sez, "I can paint her red, and red makes a beautiful job; or I can paint her a bright green, or any one of a half dozen other colors, and they're all mighty pretty; but it ain't practical to use a single solid color, and I'll tell you why. She's too durn hard to see at night. You need contrast—just like they use on them railroad crossin' bars—so you can see 'em in the dark.

"If I was you, I'd paint her a bright red, with white trimmin's—just like your barn. Then she'll match up nice in the daytime, and you can spot 'er easy at night, when you ain't got much time to go scoutin' around.

"There's a lot of fine points to puttin' up a first-class privy that the average man don't think about. It's no job for an amachoor, take my word on it. There's a whole lot more to it than you can see by just takin' a few squints at your nabor's. Why, one of the worst tragedies around here in years was because old man Clark's boys thought they knowed somethin' about this kind of work, and they didn't.

"Old man Clark—if he's a day he's ninety-seven—lives over there across the holler with his boys. Asked me to come over and estimate on their job. My price was too high; so they decided to do it themselves. And that's where the trouble begun.

"I was doin' a little paper hangin' at the time for that widder that lives down past the old creamery. As I'd drive by

I could see the boys a-workin'. Of course, I didn't want to butt in, so used to just holler at 'em on the way by and say, naborly like: 'Hey, boys, see you're doin' a little buildin'.' You see, I didn't want to act like I was buttin' in on their work; but I knowed all the time they was goin' to have trouble with that privy. And they did. From all outside appearance it was a regulation job, but not being experienced along this line, they didn't anchor her.

"You see, I put a 4 by 4 that runs from the top right straight on down five foot into the ground. That's why you never see any of my jobs upset Hallowe'en night. They might *pull* 'em out, but they'll never upset 'em.

"Here's what happened: They didn't anchor theirs, and they painted it solid red—two bad mistakes.

"Hallowe'en night come along, darker than pitch. Old man Clark was out in there. Some of them devilish nabor boys was out for no good, and they upset 'er with the old man in it.

"Of course, the old man got to callin' and his boys heard the noise. One of 'em sez: 'What's the racket? Somebody must be at the chickens.' So they took the lantern, started out to the chicken shed. They didn't find anything wrong there, and they started back to the house. Then they heerd the dog bark, and one of his boys sez, 'Sounds like that barkin' is over towards the privy.' It bein' painted red, they couldn't see she was upset, so they started over there.

"In the meantime the old man had gotten so confused that he started to crawl out through the hole, yellin' for help all the time. The boys reckonized his voice and come runnin', but just as they got there he lost his holt and fell. After that they just *called* — didn't go near him. So you see what a tragedy that was; and they tell me he has been practically ostercized from society ever since."

Well, time passed, and I finally got Elmer's job done; and, gentlemen, everybody says that, next to my eight holer, it's the finest piece of construction work in the county.

Sometimes, when I get to feelin' blue and thinkin' I hitched my wagon to the wrong star, and maybe I should have took up chiropracty or veternary, I just pack the little woman and the kids in the back of my car and start out, aimin' to fetch up at Elmer's place along about dusk.

When we gets to the top of the hill overlookin' his place, we stops. I slips the gear in mutual, and we jest sit there lookin' at that beautiful sight. There sits that privy on that knoll near the woodpile, painted red and white, mornin' glories growin' up over her and Mr. Sun bathin' her in a burst of yeller color as he drops back of them hills. You can hear the dog barkin' in the distance, bringin' the cows up fer milkin', and the slow squeak of Elmer's windmill pumpin' away day after day the same as me.

As I look at that beautiful picture of my work, I'm proud. I heaves a sigh of satisfaction, my eyes fill up and I sez to myself, "Folks are right when they say that next to my eight holer that's the finest piece of construction work I ever done. I know I done right in Specializin'; I'm sitting on top of the world; and I hope that boy of mine who is growin' up like a weed keeps up the good work when I'm gone."

With one last look as we pulls away, I slips my arm around the Missus and I sez, "Nora, Elmer don't have to worry, he's a boy that's got hisself a privy, a m-i-g-h-t-y, m-i-g-h-t-y, p-r-e-t-t-y p-r-i-v-y."

Thank you, gentlemen.

The Cup Overfloweth

This fun **Phonics** reader

belongs to

_____

Ladybird Reading

Phonics

BOOK 4

Contents

A catalogue record for this book is available from the British Library

Published by Ladybird Books Ltd
80 Strand London WC2R 0RL
A Penguin Company

2 4 6 8 10 9 7 5 3 1
© LADYBIRD BOOKS LTD MMVI
LADYBIRD and the device of a Ladybird are trademarks of Ladybird Books Ltd

ISBN-13: 978-1-84646-324-2
ISBN-10: 1-84646-324-6

Printed in Italy

Stunt Duck

by Clive Gifford
illustrated by John Haslam

introducing the **ck** letter group,
as in duck

Stunt Duck gave his jet pack one last check.

He put the jet pack on his back and locked the straps.

"Stand back,"
said Stunt Duck.

Click! He lit his jet pack with a quick flick.

Stunt Duck shot into the
bricks and blocks.

Smack! He struck the
rock at the back.

Crack! Stunt Duck hit the
deck. It all went black.

Bad luck, Stunt Duck!

Roll up!
Roll up!

by Clive Gifford
illustrated by Charlotte Combe

introducing the **ll** and **ss**
letter groups, as in well and miss

We all had a ball when the fair came to call.

Nell did well
on all the stalls.

Bess won less, but still did well.

17

The Hall of Chills was full of thrills.

19

I went wild on the
Wacky Wall.

And we sat on the
hill as evening fell.

The Sing Song Gang

by Clive Gifford
illustrated by Eric Smith

introducing the **ng** sound,
as in king

DING DONG!
BANG BANG BANG!

"Hang on!" said the King,
as the doorbell rang.

"Open up!
It's the Sing Song Gang!

Would you like us to sing
as you swing on your swing?

You can bang on the gong,

BONG

or play one of the strings."

TWANG

PING

So the gang sang a song,

and the King sang along.

HOW TO USE
Phonics
BOOK 4

This book introduces your child to words including
common groups of two or more consonants, such as
ng in the word 'king', or ck in the word 'duck'. The fun
stories will help your child begin reading simple words
containing these consonant groups.

• Read each story through to your child first.
  Familiarity helps children to identify some of the
  words and phrases.

• Have fun talking about the sounds and
  pictures together – what repeated sounds
  can your child hear in each story?

• Break new words into separate sounds
  (eg. d-u-ck) and blend their
  sounds together to say the
  word.

• Point out how words with
  the same written ending
  often rhyme. If k-ing says
  'king', what does s-ing or
  sw-ing say?

- Some common words, such as 'one', 'said' and even 'the', can't be read by sounding out. Help your child practise recognising words like these.

Phonic fun

Playing word games is a fun way to build phonic skills. Write down a consonant group and see how many words your child can think of beginning or ending with that group. For extra fun, try making up silly sentences together, using some or all of the words.

The du<u>ck</u> in his so<u>ck</u> gave Mi<u>ck</u> a sho<u>ck</u>.

Ladybird Reading

Phonics

Phonics is part of the Ladybird Reading range. It can be used alongside any other reading programme, and is an ideal way to practise the reading work that your child is doing, or about to do in school.

Ladybird has been a leading publisher of reading programmes for the last fifty years. **Phonics** combines this experience with the latest research to provide a rapid route to reading success.

The fresh quirky stories in Ladybird's twelve **Phonics** storybooks are designed to help your child have fun learning the relationship between letters, or groups of letters, and the sounds they represent.

This is an important step towards independent reading – it will enable your child to tackle new words by sounding out and blending their separate parts.